The Adventures of
Levi and Nathan
from the Cape of Cod to the
Outer Banks

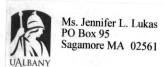

Ms. Jennifer L. Lukas
PO Box 95
Sagamore MA 02561

THE ADVENTURES
Of
LEVI and NATHAN
From the Cape of Cod to the
Outer Banks

Other Books in this Series
The Battle of Nantucket
The Adventures of Levi and Nathan
At Bassett's Island

Copyright © 1998 by
Farewell Press
Galon L. Barlow, Jr.
ISBN 0 – 9666020 – 2 – 1

Publisher
Farewell Press
P.O. Box 409, Beaufort, NC
P.O. Box 57, Buzzards Bay, MA

Printer
Griffin & Tilghman Printers, Inc.
New Bern, North Carolina

The Adventures of
Levi and Nathan
from the Cape of Cod to the
Outer Banks

The third book in a series of short adventure
Stories based on fact and Barlow
family legend.
This journey begins at the end of the book
The Adventures of Levi and Nathan
At Bassett's Island.

Written by
Galon L. Barlow, Jr.

Illustrated by
Adam C. Guthrie

A publication of
Farewell Press
Beaufort, North Carolina
(252) 728-2116
ISBN 0 – 9666020 – 2 – 1

Table of Contents

I dedicate this adventure to all of the people who devote so much of their time and energy to educate society in general about the real problems that plague the near shore habitat.

People like Tracy Warncke, of the Buzzards Bay Project, Rick Dove, a river keeper on the Neuse River, and the North Carolina Coastal Federation. To the thousands of nameless people along the coast that are trying desperately to find solutions to the many problems that society has unintentionally created. These people are the heart and soul of the coastal recovery efforts.

We say "Thank You!"

Forward

I have had the opportunity as a full time fisherman to hear many different versions of what has happened to the great schools of fish that, not that long ago, inhabited the ocean just off the East coast of the United States. As a participant in many fishing activities, I feel that it is important for society to know what a fisherman has seen taking place.

Our industry is based on renewable resources. These resources need certain conditions to survive. We as a society must put our thoughts together to find the ways to recover and protect our near shore habitat for all.

Introduction

Levi and Nathan are brothers who became spirits shortly after an encounter with a terrible storm that took place in the fall of the year 1782. They have become time travelers and are now in the year 1998 and have returned to their homeport on the Cape of Cod. Levi and his brother Nathan have met a descendant of theirs, Old Galon, and another spirit too, Grace, a middle aged lady spirit who has agreed to join their journey.

At the end of their last adventure, Old Galon has just become a spirit and has been returned to Bassett's Island to see if he can join the crew of the Speedwell, the legendary pirate ship that Levi and his group are sailing to the South for the winter. Let's return to Bassett's Island and join with this unlikely band of coastal mariners.

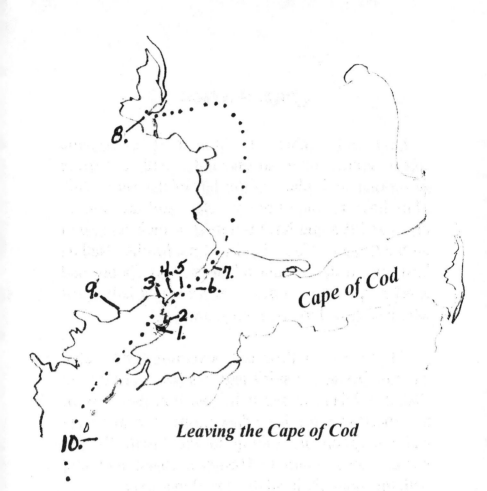

Leaving the Cape of Cod

1. **Bassett's Island**
2. **Wings Neck**
3. **Massachusetts Maritime Academy**
4. **Train Bridge**
5. **Bourne Bridge**
6. **Sagamore Bridge**
7. **Power Plant**
8. **Plymouth Harbor**
9. **Onset**
10. **Cuttyhunk Island**

Chapter One

The Speedwell's crew has just observed the spirit of Old Galon being brought to Bassett's Island to join them. He is ashore, upon the beach waiting for someone to come for him with the longboat. Levi quickly climbs down into the rowboat and heads for shore. As the boat comes near the beach Old Galon speaks to Levi.

"I'm a spirit now Levi, and I would like to join your crew for a time, if you have room for me."

"I don't think that is a problem, Galon. But first, what happened to bring on your demise so suddenly?"

"Oh Levi, that's a story for another time, but smoking all those cigarettes certainly made my golden years much more difficult."

"Well, come on Galon, let us get back to the Speedwell and start our voyage. You'll have to share the cabin in the stern with Nathan and I. Grace has moved into the quarters in the bow. That area of the ship has never been so clean. She is amazing!"

The longboat quickly approached the Speedwell. Nathan reached down to grab the bowline of the longboat from Galon.

"Welcome aboard!" Grace bellowed, to the old man.

"This is the last place I expected to see you!"

"I'm sure you're as surprised as I was," replied Galon. "I didn't plan this, ya know."

"None of us did," exclaimed Nathan.

"Well, we are all in the same boat now!!!!"

Levi laughs.

"We certainly are Nathan and I am sure we will make the best of it. Let us raise the sails, haul the anchor, and begin our voyage to learn what other great changes society has cast upon the sea."

Chapter Two

The tide is still rising as the Speedwell leaves the area known as the Mill Pond, at Bassett's Island, and enters upper Buzzards Bay. Galon asks Levi if he's really that interested in the many changes that have taken place since his time.

"Oh yes! The sea has always been a part of my heritage. I surely want to help protect it, if I can." Levi replied quickly.

"Perhaps we should take the time to sail East through the Cape Cod Canal before we head South. There are things of interest that you may enjoy seeing. It wouldn't take long and I think both you and Nathan would enjoy the tour." The old man suggested.

"Let's do it," exclaims Nathan. We have plenty of time, and Galon certainly knows the way."

"Okay Galon, take the helm and show us some of the changes." Levi agrees.

Galon steps behind the old steering wheel. As he grasps the wooden spokes he can almost feel the warmth and spirit of the vessel flow through his soul. He will relax now and guide this graceful old sloop through out the local waters that he knows so well.

The ship comes slowly around Wings Neck and both the Barlow brothers become aware of the many changes in the local channels, caused by the digging of the Cape Cod Canal.

Chapter Three

Grace calls to Nathan.

"Let's climb into the rigging to enjoy the scenery."

"That sounds like a great idea," replied Nathan.

Quickly they scrambled up the rigging that secures the mast, sitting high upon the lower crossbeam of the topsail. From this vantage point their view of the surrounding area increased dramatically. The channel from Wings Neck on through the Canal was relatively straight and clearly marked. There is little boating traffic this time of year so the vessel moves along smoothly between some small islands in the area. After the first group of islands is passed, a large ship comes into view, just beyond are some large bridges.

"Galon, what are all these ships and buildings and bridges?"

"Actually, Levi, this first ship coming into view is the Patriot State, the training ship of the Massachusetts Navy, and the buildings are the Massachusetts Maritime Academy. Next, is a railroad lift bridge, one of the largest in the world, and in the distance, over there, is a bridge for cars and trucks.

These bridges have a clearance of 135 feet from the water to the bottom of the bridge. During the years between your lifetime and mine there were many sailing ships built that would never fit under these giant bridges. My grandfather, his name was Edward, sailed a large ship like that. She was the Jesse, a three masted schooner that traded throughout the Atlantic Ocean. He was particularly fond of traveling to South America. The ship displaced 400 tons and was one of the last Coastal Traders that sailed to tie up to the wharf at Barlow's Landing.

My Father got his Master's License under sail too, but quickly changed over to steam. Now there are all sorts of power plants to move ships."

Thinking for a moment, Levi then asks.

"This Massachusetts Navy, is this the same basic idea that we had back during the Revolutionary War?"

"Not really," replies the old man. "You volunteered your ships and time to fight for what you believed in. Today the standards and beliefs are as high as ever, but training is more towards engineering and the merchant marine. Technology has come a long way in the past two centuries and people are just now beginning to feel the consequences of our progress."

"What do you mean, consequences?"

"I mean, the results of a fast changing society, always seeking a better or easier way to accomplish a given task. You'll understand in time, Levi."

"Are you talking about the bottom paint? Like on that large ship that we just passed?"

"No, Levi, I wasn't. But now that you bring it up. The government in its weird wisdom has done some strange things with laws since your day."

"Like what?"

"Well, take bottom paint for instance. Commercial ships and government vessels are allowed to use an even more toxic type of paint than the average boater. This allows a person to think that the bottom paint he uses on his pleasure boat is not toxic. But all they have to do is read the label on the can to learn how very toxic it actually is. Not only don't they read the labels, but most people don't bother to even take the proper precautions while handling and applying this paint!"

"Wow," said Levi. The time has come when nearly everyone can read and many people don't bother. Times have certainly changed!"

Grace and Nathan are enjoying their bird's eye view from high in the rigging still.

Now the ship is in the land cut of the Canal. In the fall of the year the leaves in this area change color. The scenery is breathtaking; the rolling hills

7

**The Power Plant on the Cape Cod
Canal as seen by Levi, Nathan and
Grace as Galon guides them down
the Canal.**

of the area are blazing with the sharp colors of autumn; brilliant reds blend with gold, orange and yellows. The greens of the pine trees only seem to bring out the colors more. The fiery colors in the distance gently blend with the dark blue waters of the Canal. Nathan and Grace both look on in awe of the beauty before them.

The ship moves on at a good pace sailing under both bridges, through a couple long curves and under another bridge, very similar in appearance to the first auto bridge. Shortly after passing this second bridge a huge smokestack rises into the sky on their right.

Galon knows that Levi will soon be full of questions so he just starts off explaining.

"That's a power plant. A place to generate electrical energy from other fuels. The electricity is delivered everywhere through wires. This is far to complicated for me, but it works well and most everyone uses this type of power in these times."

"But why is their so much smoke?" Asks Levi.

"Well, this is another weird government law. If these plants burn a clean type of fuel for a time, then they can burn a real dirty fuel for another given amount of time, polluting the air terribly."

Now past the power plant the ship enters the open waters of Cape Cod Bay. Levi begins to look around and knows immediately where he is.

"Galon, is the old Sandwich Harbor located right over there?" Levi asks, pointing toward some sand dunes.

"Why sure it is." Galon nods and replies.

"Then Plymouth Harbor is just north of here around the next point, right?"

"Yes it is. Would you like to take a quick look at Plymouth to see if you notice any major changes since your time?"

"Oh Galon, I do not think it could have changed too much. Plymouth has been a busy port since the Pilgrims first settled there."

"I don't know Levi, the world has certainly changed a lot in the past hundred years."

"Okay Galon, lets take a quick trip to Plymouth, but then we must get started on our trip South."

Galon slowly turns the ship north and sails far offshore, for the coast is very rocky and treacherous in this area. Nathan and Grace are intirqued watching the giant blue fin tuna in the area. These fish weigh in at over a thousand pounds each. Looking down from high in the rigging these fish are easily spotted just below the surface of the crisp, clear waters of Cape Cod Bay.

"Wow!" Nathan exclaims. "Grace, this is great. I love to watch these fish."

"Me too. The tuna season is closed now and these fish are fattening themselves up for the long journey to their winter home."

"Where is that?"

"I'm not sure, but some of them winter far offshore, east of the Outer Banks of North Carolina. Perhaps we'll come across these fish again later on in our journey."

Rounding the high cliffs of land bordering this part of Cape Cod Bay the entrance to Plymouth Harbor comes into view. At the same time so does another power plant. A little different to look at but, undoubtedly a power plant. Galon watches Levi's reaction before speaking.

"Galon, where is the smoke stack?" Queries Levi.

"Well, this is really, really beyond my comprehension, but this is called a Nuclear Power Plant. It burns a smokeless fuel and is very powerful. So powerful that a slight miscalculation could bring on a monumental disaster. But on the other hand, if this power is properly harnessed, cheap, clean power is available. Today's society is very questionable about this type of power. Perhaps soon scientists and engineers will feel more comfortable with how this fuel and power is handled."

"If this is beyond your understanding, you certainly must know of my confusion." Spoke Levi.

Galon brings the Speedwell around the outer bar and through the narrow channel into Plymouth

Harbor. Grace and Nathan have climbed down from the rigging and are now in the bow watching for shallow water. An old lighthouse marks the entrance and a sandbar is right behind it. Knowing this Galon turns the ship quickly to the left, follows the channel for a short distance, then he calls for Nathan to drop the anchor.

Grace and Nathan quickly drop anchor as the Speedwell comes up into the wind. The sails go slack and the crew races to lower the main sail. Then the topsail is slackened so it just flaps in the breeze.

Looking up into the rigging the old man swells with pride at the sight of their family flag signaling their presence.

"Too bad no one can see us," he thinks to himself.

The long boat is lowered and they all climb down into it to explore the harbor. Slowly Levi rows down the channel and comes around a breakwater. An old sailing ship sits at a dock in the distance.

"What is this?" Levi asks.

"Why it's a replica of the Mayflower!" Blurts out Grace. "Plymouth has become an important part of history, you know. There are museums and even the Plimouth Plantation, a village that is exactly as the Pilgrims lived hundreds of years ago.

You do know that Thanksgiving is now a national holiday?"

"Not really," says Nathan. "What do people do to celebrate this holiday?"

"Why we eat of course." Grace added and laughed. "We eat and thank God for all the blessings that he has bestowed upon us."

Nathan is beaming.

"A whole day for just eating! What a life!"

"You are missing the point Nathan. Thanksgiving - be thankful - Ya know!"

"Well," speaks the old man. "I've watched this holiday turn into a day to spend watching football on television, rather than with one's family. Times are really changing rapidly and family life is changing too."

"Lets get back to the task at hand and explore this harbor. I don't want to row through this great fleet of boats moored here. Let us go back around that jetty and walk across those exposed flats." Levi suggests.

"In our day there were many clams and shellfish here." Nathan notes. "Flounder too."

"No doubt there was," replies Galon.

As the boat comes to a halt, aground, they all climb out to walk around. First dragging their longboat upon the bar.

"This place is a muck hole now. Why?"

"You must remember, times have changed. Government is not famous for making real good decisions all the time. When pumps and plumbing made running water available to most every home, the waste had to be dealt with. First cesspools were dug, but they soon overflowed with water and some waste. So septic systems were designed and they eventually began to fail also.

Then another genius claimed that sewerage could be cleaned up and treated in a plant and the toxins removed so well, that you could drink the treated water. He should have been required to drink it! This so called - clean water is then dumped in the harbor. A nice thought but as soon as too many homes are hooked up to this type of system it can overload and then toxins and waste are dumped directly through a pipe into the harbor.

These systems have been built in most coastal areas and frequently overload or break down and dump directly into the nursery areas killing millions of fish and shellfish larvae. Because this harbor has such a small entrance, the volume of water exchange with the ocean is not great enough to dilute these toxins. This harbor, which thirty years ago, was one of the most productive in the land, is now simply an extension of a sewer system. But never fear..." The old man goes on.

"Newer technology is at hand. Boston now uses ocean out-fall. In other words, they have extended their sewer pipe far offshore. In a very few years, far more of the ocean's bottom will be affected by these toxins and wastes that now plague the near shore area."

"Why doesn't someone design a system that uses far less water? That is what we did." Levi questioned.

"Oh, that would be too easy. Technology does not work well with simple solutions." Grace quickly added.

"The way of the world today, is to use all the fresh water, pollute the near shore habitat, and then find someone to blame. That's your people, Galon. The commercial fishermen must have caught all the fish..." and she laughed.

"Not so quick Grace! The commercial fishermen are always blamed when there are problems in the ocean. This is a terrible injustice. It's like blaming the Indians for killing all the buffalo."

Nathan, shocked, declares, "The buffalo are gone?"

"Sure Nathan," answers Grace. "Sportsmen killed off the buffalo, a hundred years ago."

"Why?"

"They killed them for the fun of it and blamed the Indians. Time told the truth, but it was to late for the buffalo."

Nathan is terribly upset that Plymouth Harbor is polluted.

A tear appeared in Nathan's eye as he spoke in a broken tone.

"I always wanted to see a buffalo."

"Well those days are gone, Nathan. So toughen up!" Spits Grace, trying to break his depression.

Nathan is becoming furious. He stoops, scoops a handful of muck, and he throws it as far as he can. And continues to stomp and begins scream.

"WHAT IS WRONG WITH PEOPLE? WHERE ARE THE CLAMS! THE FISH! WAKE UP PLEASE! TAKE RESPONSIBILITY!!!"

Levi runs over to Nathan, wraps his arm around his brother, and speaks softly.

"Calm down, calm down Nathan. No one can hear us now. It's too late."

"I know Levi. I know." Nathan replies. Calming down.

While they walk back across the flats towards the longboat Galon explains further.

"Until about thirty years ago this harbor was open for the trawling of nets by commercial fishermen. This type of activity stirred up a lot of this mud allowing it moved upstream and down. Lots of oxygen was churned into these waters at the same time. Fish production was good. Weekend fishermen, ignorant of what was taking place, yet very jealous of the commercial catches, banded together and had this area closed for their own exclusive use. Now it is all dead bottom and no one catches hardly a thing in this muck hole of a harbor - many locals proudly call Plymouth, "America's Home Town". They haven't been out on the clam flats for awhile."

Upon reaching the longboat Levi is still asking questions.

"Why would the harbor be closed to trawling if trawling were good?"

"It's all politics, Levi. It's about the number of votes a certain group of people can amass. It has nothing to do with right or wrong... It's simply the numbers of people that support a particular user group. The people that held office when the harbor was closed to trawling are long gone and no one accepts the responsibility of this mess."

Pushing the longboat back into the channel they all jump in. Levi rows slowly across the channel looking at the town, remembering what a productive and vibrant harbor she had been.

"For the most part Plymouth's historic inner harbor is simply a parking lot for boats." Levi speaks his thoughts out loud.

Reaching the Speedwell Grace scrambles aboard fastening the line. The others are right behind her.

"Let us raise the longboat and secure it tightly. It will be almost a thousand miles before we lower it again." Levi suggests.

Once this task is complete Grace climbs into the rigging to secure the topsail, while Galon and Nathan turn the old windlass to raise the anchor high. Nathan secures the flukes of the anchor to the bowsprit for the long voyage South. Levi and Nathan now hoist the mainsail back up, while the old man is back at the helm guiding the ship slowly out of the harbor.

Grace and Nathan then climb back into the rigging to watch for whales and giant tuna. The sloop is moving swiftly now, as sailing in familiar territory always makes time go by faster.

Soon the Speedwell is back in the Cape Cod Canal. Approaching the western end of the Canal the day is coming to an end.

"Levi, why don't we tie up for the night and get a fresh start in the morning?" Asks Galon.

"Sure, tie us up where ever you would like."

"There is a small harbor along the way called Onset. We can tie to the pier, unseen and spend the night."

"This is gonna be great," Grace tells Nathan.

"I know this village. We can walk around and I'll show you the sights."

Soon the vessel is secured to the dock and both Galon and Levi want to get some rest. Grace and Nathan decide to walk about this small coastal town.

Nathan and Grace in Onset,
peering in the Pizza Parlor.

Walking across the wharf Grace asks Nathan not let her forget to take him up there and she points up at the top of the bluff that skirts a most beautiful beach.

On the main street now the first shop that they come to is a pizza parlor. Nathan has never seen one before and peers through the window watching a man making pizzas; tossing the spinning dough gently into the air, then covering the large pie with a brilliant red sauce, sprinkling on cheese and a variety of meats and vegetables, then slowly cooking these delightful treats. It smelled so good. Nathan's mouth began to water. Grace had to snap him out of his trance.

"Knock it off! We don't need to eat! Remember?"

"So what is next, Grace?"

"An Ice Cream Parlor, Nathan. We'd better cross the street."

Grace grabbed Nathan's arm and quickly pulled him across the street. Nathan now peers into a shop named "Tales to Tell."

"What's that Grace?"

"A book shop."

Grace looks in and laughs sighting a giant figure of a rabbit dressed in a blue topcoat, holding a book as if he is reading it.

"Don't worry Nathan, that's not real."

"Wow!" Says Nathan. "Look at all the books.

This is like a library. Can we get some books for the boat, Grace, can we?"

"I don't think so, Nathan, but lets look around back. Perhaps we can find some."

Grace finds a trash barrel and looks down inside. She reaches in and removes some slightly soiled books.

"How about these, Nathan?" And she handed him a half dozen tattered books and some magazines with their covers torn off.

"This is great. We have not had new books to read for years. Levi will be excited at our find. Let's hurry back to the boat to show him."

As they walk down the street back towards the pier Grace remembered her treat on the bluff for Nathan.

"Come this way," she says.

They walked over the hill, past a gazebo, and to the very top of the bluff overlooking the harbor. Nathan scanned the area and remarked.

"What a beautiful view this is."

"Look there, Nathan. Behind you."

He turned to see a beautiful bronze sculpture of a young Indian Maiden. She is looking across the harbor also. The inscription mentions that her ancestors had fished and lived here for 10,000 years. Nathan had to look closely to see the tears in her eyes, but they are there.

"Onset, the beginning place," he thought to himself.

Grace poked him.

"Come on Nathan, let's get back to the boat."

Chapter Four

While Grace and Nathan have gone sightseeing Old Galon and Levi have been laying in hammocks in the stern of the Speedwell conversing as they rested.

"Galon," questioned Levi. "When we were on Bassett's Island you told me that the bay scallops in this area have all but disappeared."

"Ayah, that they have," replied the old man.

"Did you notice any other odd changes that may have contributed to the failure of this crop?" Prodded Levi.

"Well yes, I suppose I did. It's a lengthy story are you sure you'd want to hear it now?"

"Sure I do. I enjoy your thoughts immensely."

"Well as you already know, I earned my keep as a shellfisherman. My wife Rita and I would scallop almost every winter to provide for our family. It was a good living and our family all participated in the handling of the scallops in one way or another. Some shucked and cleaned the scallops; while others cleaned the shed and emptied the barrels of the shells that accumulated daily. Those were the days. Scallops were usually quite plentiful and we had our secret spots too for late in the season.

During the years 1974-75 a different kind of weed started to grow in the area. This weed attached itself to shellfish and rocks. The fishermen grew concerned and went to the state. The biologists for the state claimed it was a new weed that came to this area in the bilges of ships from Asia, or maybe even from a child's aquarium. But never the less this so called *"exotic"* thrived here. Codium was its scientific name. "Spike Grass" is what we called it."

Soon growers of oysters were claiming that this weed would lift oysters up and float them away. I never observed this myself, but I did pay attention to this new menace and our scallop beds.

Scallops in some areas were so covered with this weed that their growth became stunted. One year, Nantucket lost its entire crop, due to this new predator.

During the next few years this problem grew. Scallops had such growths of this weed on them that it became a major job just removing it as the scallops were harvested.

As time passed I watched this weed much more closely. In the spring of the year, when scallop seed was small, this weed would grow attached to the shell. The weed grew rapidly, becoming tumbleweed in the ocean itself. Areas with large amounts of scallop seed would be rolled along on the bottom because of the tumbleweed effect of this growth. The shellfish would all end up deposited in the low spots in the area. The seed would be piled together and unable to move around due to this added growth. The bay scallop beds diminished in size rapidly.

In a couple years time many beds in tidal areas disappeared completely. Recent studies seem to indicate that if shellfish larvae don't find evidence of a former shellfish bed in an area then the larvae are less likely to settle in that area.

So my thoughts are that maybe this "exotic" has had a much greater part in hindering bay scallop reproduction than the first problems of smothering the shellfish and reducing its growth.

This weed may have actually stripped many scallop beds of any evidence of scallop essence, so to speak.

Of course, this is my own personal theory.

So Levi, "exotics" may be very harmful and must be monitored very carefully. This is just one example of many "exotics". This one shows how even a plant that appears very harmless can cause havoc, unseen in the ocean."

The Speedwell rocks gently as Grace and Nathan climb back aboard the sloop. As the hammocks swing Nathan enters the cabin.

A Bay Scallop with Codium attached.
An "exotic" plant this codium is known for
moving many beds of shellfish.

"I've got new books, Levi. I can't wait for the next Nor' Easter."

Nathan slips the books under the bunk for safekeeping.

"How was your walk?" Levi asks.

"Great. We saw a Pizza Shop and watched them cook from the window."

"What else did you see?"

"A very beautiful sculpture of an Indian Maiden. She appeared to be weeping, to me. Saddened at the loss of her heritage, I'm sure.

Levi, I really liked the Pizza Shop. If we ever come back to Onset I'm going to spend more time watching those men cook.

Grace has gone to her cabin for the night and I'm going to retire to my hammock now. Good night." And Nathan was off.

"Good night boys," says the old man.

Chapter Five

Both Levi and Galon arise before the sun the next morning. Galon feels a little uneasy about leaving the area. Here he is sure to see some of his children now and then. His sons are both local shellfishermen. On the other hand the winters here are long and bleak, he thinks to himself.

Levi and Galon are quick to raise all of the sails and take their lines aboard. Casting off, they are underway, slowly returning to the Cape Cod Canal, then southwest through Buzzards Bay, and into the ocean. After clearing Cuttyhunk Island, the last of the island chain in area, Levi sets a course for the Carolina coast.

Galon is still at the wheel when Grace comes on deck.

"Morning." She says, as she walks to the bow and sits in the sun.

Nathan soon comes out on deck from the aft cabin, and begins to stretch.

"OH ME!" He yawns.

"What does that mean?" Queries Galon.

"What? OH ME? It just means I'm old and tired."

"Well in that case, OOOHHHHHH MEEEEEEE!" Says the old man, laughing.

Levi sits upon a cannon watching the seagulls circling a school of fish. Occasionally a gull will dive into the water to catch a fish. Levi rises and walks back to Old Galon.

"So tell me, what has really become of the huge schools of fish that lived in the ocean, offshore here?"

"I know it is hard to believe, Levi, but until 25 years ago the largest fishing fleets in the world fished just offshore here. They were virtually unregulated. Using modern technology these huge fleets from countries like Russia, Portugal, Italy and many others, harvested fish from George's Banks and all the other great fishing areas of the Northeast. They did this harvesting much faster than these species of fish could recover. This combined with the loss of most of the near shore nursery area has driven many species population's down. But fish stocks can recover quickly if the near shore environment is cleaned up and no "exotic" species come along.

The most important lesson from this is that society always needs a scapegoat. Once again the local fishermen of the Northeast caught the blame for this disaster. Even though the fishermen predicted it years ago and pleaded for limits to be placed on the offshore harvest of fish by foreign fleets.

The complaints from fishermen about "*shoddy coastal development*" have almost always been ignored too. People who don't participate in a business like fishing have a very difficult time understanding the ups and downs of cycles in stocks. Many species are predators of other fish and shellfish, to say nothing of disease; all this has to be factored in too. Fish stocks can fluctuate dramatically because they are supposed to do exactly that. People have no problem seeing a farmer plant different crops each year to keep his soil from growing weary, yet they can't understand the need for a fisherman to have the ability to switch fisheries at will. Society just can't seem to relate to a fisherman's lifestyle at all. This inability to understand leads to many social problems in time."

"Social problems?" Asks Levi.

"For lack of a better name, that's what I call them.

So Levi, are we going straight across the open ocean to the Carolina coast?" He continues.

"Yes, Galon, unless you know a better way."

"Well, there is the Inland Waterway that runs from Cape Cod to Florida. This is a chain of man made canals that connects various sounds and bays. It is possible to navigate almost all of the

East Coast without entering the ocean, but we have no charts aboard, and we would need them to go that way."

"Do not even give it a thought my friend," assures Levi. "We'll be alright crossing the open water in this ship. The Speedwell is a well-built vessel. I am not sure how my father acquired her, being in the "Pirate" trade and all. He brought many treasures home and no one ever asked their origin. I believe that she was built in North Carolina though. Many of these Bermuda Sloops were built there. This one is built of long leaf yellow pine, a very tough wood that was used in Southern shipbuilding.

This ship had to be tough to stand up to the pounding it got during the *Battle of Nantucket*. The British had us broadside and fired their cannons directly on us several times. Most vessels would have been completely destroyed, but not this one!"

Galon agrees with a nod and a smile as he loosens the lines allowing the boom to swing out so the sail will catch more air. The wind is blowing briskly from the Northwest. The sky is a brilliant blue with a few fluffy white clouds. The small Bermuda Sloop is really moving nicely through the open ocean now.

Grace and Nathan are ready to return to their place in the rigging to enjoy the sights. Land has faded into the distance.

It is early afternoon when Nathan points out what appears to be a large scow towed by another smaller boat in the distance.

"Grace, do you see that ship?

"Well, of course I do, Nathan."

"I mean, what is it?"

"I think it's probably a garbage barge."

"Why would a garbage barge be way out here in the ocean, Grace?"

"Well, Nathan, there is a lot of garbage now-a-days and it's legal to dump it a certain distance offshore, out in the ocean. So some companies do."

"Come on Grace. We better go down and talk to Levi."

"You go Nathan, I'm sure you can tell him as well as I. I'm pretty comfortable right here for the time being."

"Okay, I'll be back in a while."

As Nathan reaches the deck he calls for Levi. He comes walking forward and they both sit upon the windlass on the bow.

"So Nathan, is there a problem?"

"Well Levi, sort of. See that old scow being towed in the distance?"

"Yes, I see it."

A garbage barge being towed off shore.
There the garbage will be dumped into
the ocean.

"Well Levi, it is full of garbage! They dump it in the ocean now. We are sailing in the DUMP, Levi! Can you believe it? These people collect all their sewerage together and spill it into the ocean, and now we see that they also haul some of their garbage offshore and dump this also. What is wrong?! What are people thinking?"

"I am not sure Nathan. This is not the world we knew."

The sun is getting low in the sky. Levi goes back to relieve the old man.

"Galon, why not take a break, sit and relax. I'll take the wheel for a spell."

"That will be nice. It's been a long day for me. I've not sailed like this for many years."

"I figure that we will make about 12 knots at best. With a fair wind we should make Cape Hatteras in three days, or so."

"Perhaps," agrees the old man, "but you know the weather in the North Atlantic."

"Oh, I certainly do," answers Levi. "It can change rapidly, and if we are not careful we could end up in big trouble quickly."

"Well, we could if we were still mortals. I can't imagine what would happen to us. Jhonna was swallowed by a whale and spit upon the beach."

"That doesn't sound like a lot of fun."

"No Levi, but I think we'll be okay. There must be a higher purpose to our being here. Otherwise we would have gone on to our final resting place like most people, or spirits I mean."

As the sun sets Grace climbs down from the rigging, and walks back to the stern.

"This could get kind of boring after a time." She says.

"Grace, tomorrow if you would like, you could clean the stern cabin. It sure could use it."

"Sure, I'd love to! She perks right up.

"I'll retire early so I'll be all rested up. Hey Nathan, rest well tonight, tomorrow you can help me by lugging all the heavy stuff."

Nathan walking back to the stern cabin shakes his head slowly and sighs.

"Oh Me!"

Galon is not far behind. Levi will run the ship through the night. The wind is still brisk from the Northwest and things are going very smooth and easy. The clear sky is beginning to become brighter with the appearance of stars. Oh what a beautiful fall night. The moon has begun its journey across the sky, not quite full, but very bright.

As Levi looks out across the deck, through the night he realizes that maybe the old man is right. Maybe there is a purpose to their being here. Why would he and his brother have been brought through time like this?

"What good will come of our knowledge of society's mistakes?" Levi speaks softly.

Levi passes the night lost in thought.

Chapter Six

As the sun rises, so does Galon.

"Good morning Levi."

"Yes it certainly is, Galon. And if you would take the wheel I would surly like to rest a little before every one is up and about. There will be no rest once Grace attacks our cabin, you know!!!"

He heads for his hammock for a short rest.

Galon watches the gulls flying around looking for food.

"They never land upon the boat. They must not see it. This is real strange. There must be more spirits somewhere." The old man thinks to himself.

Soon Nathan is upon the deck to keep Galon company.

"Galon, why do people dump the garbage in the ocean?"

"Well, Nathan there aren't too many cities that do that, but it is allowed by society, because it's a cheap way to dispose of waste."

"Does it ever wash up on the beach?"

"Oh yes. It surely does, usually in the form of medical needles and other plastics. But sometimes after bad storms, coastal areas become littered with tons of garbage and waste. All kinds of stuff. What a mess! Well Nathan, here comes Grace."

"Morning boys. Are you ready to do some work Nathan?"

"I suppose so, Grace."

Levi hearing everyone on deck arises. He walks out on the deck and stretches his hands high in the air and sighs saying.

"Oh Nathan!!!!"

Nathan asks quickly. "Why did you say Oh Nathan?"

"Because you have to move all the stuff for Grace." He laughs.

Levi walks forward to sit upon a cannon.

"It is all yours Grace."

Grace with a big grin tells Nathan.

"Come on, let's get to it!"

Soon Nathan is dragging all the loose stuff out of the cabin in the stern. Everything not nailed down is on deck.

Grace ties a rope to a bucket and has Nathan throw it in the ocean to get water to wash the cabin down. Next she takes all the bedding and hangs it all about the ship. The pillows are thrown upon the bow. Grace now asks Nathan to stand clear and leave her to clean the cabin up.

Nathan didn't have to hear that twice. He headed to the bow where Levi laid on his back with a pillow to comfort his head.

"This looks like the place to be." Said Nathan as he grabbed a pillow and found a comfortable spot in the sun.

The day went by swiftly, and it wasn't long before Grace was calling for help to move the heavy stuff back inside the cabin. Levi went to help Nathan this time so Grace would be free to shake out the bedding.

Everything was clean and smelled so good. Levi quickly looked under his bunk to check for his books and the charts stored there.

Some of these charts are copies of the charts drawn of the Carolina coast, centuries ago, by an ancestor of the Barlow family, Arthur Barlowe. Arthur had explored the area for Sir Walter Raleigh in 1584. Somewhere aboard the Speedwell was a copy of the narrative Arthur Barlowe had written about his findings. This narrative was instrumental in the further exploration of this area.

Nathan was now lugging in bedding and such.

"Levi, we better get out of here, she is coming back to make the beds."

"Okay Nathan. Lets go sit with Galon while Grace finishes up."

Levi and Nathan are back by the steering wheel with Galon, and the three continue to converse. The wheel is actually above the stern quarters where Grace is still busy.

"Galon, I can't wait until you see the cabin," speaks Nathan.

"I'm sure it's fine," quickly adds the old man.

"Oh no Galon, it is much cleaner than 'just fine'! I tell you, that woman is amazing! The cabin almost glows." Levi adds with excitement.

"I'll soon find out. It has been another long day for me. I'm getting better at standing all day at the wheel, but it does wear me down."

"I will do a turn tomorrow at the wheel," offers Nathan.

"Sounds good to me!" Replies Galon.

Grace appears on deck.

"All set!" She yells to the men. "I've had it for the day. I'll see you all in the morning."

And she disappeared into her cabin.

Just then Galon slipped a piece of line on one of the spokes of the wheel.

"That'll hold the wheel steady. Let's go look at our cabin."

As the three men entered the cabin they could hardly believe what they saw. Not only was it clean and neat, but there were curtains hung around the windows in the stern, and they were clean! Grace had taken a rag and tied it together with string to make it appear as a flower; this had been hung on the wall above the desk at which the Captain kept his records.

They all agreed that this was great and they would do their best to keep things organized.

"Galon, you may as well stay here and rest. It is time for my watch anyway."

Levi heads back on deck to guide the ship for the night. Both Galon and Nathan are exhausted and waste no time climbing into their hammocks to relax.

The Speedwell plows through the night. Some how the air seems clearer to Levi. The stars twinkle boldly while the moonbeams seem to glisten in their wake. The ship sails along so effortlessly that Levi begins to daydream once again. Foremost in his thoughts are all these changes that society has brought upon itself. Thinking out loud again Levi softly speaks.

"Where will all this madness end? What great disaster will occur to get society's attention?"

As Levi thinks the night passes and the moon moves across the sky. As the moon begins her decent and early morning light starts to appear there is a time that is so quiet that Levi feels as though he is alone against the world. Feeling that he must do something to bring attention to these problems. Not like Nathan when he throws his tantrums, but something, someway he must cross this dimension and state his case.

Chapter Seven

"Levi!"

Startled, Levi jumps. Galon is up and about.

"Levi, you are exhausted? Go rest. I can take the helm till Nathan gets about."

Levi agrees and heads for his hammock. The old man is in his glory, sailing this old sloop into a new era. Looking about the vessel he realizes how truly beautiful this old sloop really is. She is pure and free from the clutter modern ship's have. There are no electronics, no power, nothing but a compass and the old sextant that Levi occasionally takes a reading with at noon. Then Levi will hurry into the cabin to figure his readings. No one has any idea what he is doing, but he seems to know where they are going.

Grace is upon the deck with her broom and begins to sweep the deck in the bow. Nathan wanders on deck and stretches, yawning and speaking to all.

"Morning everyone." And nods.

"Good morning Nathan. Are you ready to take your watch?" Questions Galon.

"Sure I am. I will be right there."

Soon Nathan is behind the wheel. Now Galon is free for the day.

"I really want to look the cannons over. I've never seen guns like these."

"Go ahead," says Nathan. "They are pretty simple to operate. We have plenty of powder aboard stored away, but we used all the cannon balls at the Battle of Nantucket."

"I don't want to fire them, I just want to study them."

Galon spends the rest of the morning disassembling one of the Speedwell's cannons to see how they are made.

Grace relieves Nathan at the wheel and watches Galon tinker for awhile. Galon now has cannon parts all around the area. He is cleaning and checking all the parts for their condition. Grace has never been very fond of guns and gets bored quickly with Galon and his project. Soon she gives the watch back to Nathan and climbs back into the rigging to enjoy the ocean about them. Galon never enjoyed trying to do projects with people looking on anyway.

Soon he was putting the cannon back together, while slowly inspecting each piece as if he was back in the Navy.

About noon Grace spotted a boat off in the distance. To her it looks like a large power boat.

"Nathan," she yells, swing over that way, pointing in the direction of the sporty looking craft.

The yell has awakened Levi, and he is out on deck walking toward the bow. Galon is just finishing the assembly of the first cannon he has cleaned. The old man looks at Levi and declares.

"She's as good as new."

Levi smiles as he walks by.

"Let's hope we never have to fire the cannons again! We have no shot aboard."

Galon gets to his feet and walks with Levi to the bow. Grace walks back and offers to take a short watch so Nathan might go to the bow too.

"I'm going to swing close to that boat so we can watch them," says Grace.

Closing in on the boat, Galon realizes what type of boat it is.

"This is your first glance at sports fishing. This is a charter boat. Lots of power, fast and stable. People hire this type of boat to take them offshore fishing. It is a rapidly growing industry in some parts of the country.

"So what do they fish for?" Asks Nathan.

"This time of year? Well some of those giant tuna are probably in the vicinity."

"I thought you told us that fishery was closed."

"Yes, it's closed but these people are probably using a technique called "catch and release". It's a new fad that another marketing genius recently dreamed up.

Imagine this, people hook a fish, fight it till it's completely worn down, they sometimes put a gaff in it's gills to hold it, then they remove the hook from the fish's damaged mouth and set it free. Think about it... this is the fish's only way to eat. A fish has no hands, and their mouth is usually damaged."

"Look," says Grace. "The man strapped to the chair in the stern of the sports boat has a fish hooked."

They watch for an hour as the man fights the fish. As the fish becomes tired and weak, the man manages to get it alongside their boat. Reaching over the side someone grabs the giant fish by its gills, tearing it open, while blood spews all about in the water.

"What a shame," speaks the old man.

"Fish breath by using their gills. That's like someone ripping out one of your lungs."

Sharks nearby pick up on the scent of blood in the water immediately and head for the tuna.

Nathan is now climbing the rigging. Halfway up he stops and looks towards the sports boat. He is so furious he is shaking. He screams with all his might.

"WHAT IS WRONG WITH YOU? CATCH 'EM. CLEAN 'EM. COOK 'EM AND EAT 'EM! THAT'S WHAT FISHING IS ALL ABOUT!!!"

Releasing the giant fish the men jump back as they hear a terrible wailing noise in the wind. Looking about they see nothing, but they decide to leave anyway.

Nathan slowly climbs back down from the rigging. Old Galon speaks up.

"Nathan, something is wrong. You are getting more upset all the time about things. There is nothing we can do. Yet it looked like you almost screamed through a dimension of time."

"Sure did!" Grace agreed and spoke to Levi.

"Take the watch. I think I know what Nathan's problem is."

Both Levi and Galon looked a little bewildered.

"What do you mean Grace?" Asked Nathan.

"Do you think there is something wrong with me?"

"I'm sure there is Nathan. Why a couple days ago you threw a fit in Plymouth, and now this. Nathan, you haven't eaten for days. You need some jelly to cheer you up."

Nathan begins to grin as Grace quickly heads down into her cabin. Returning in a flash.

"I just realized that I have your jelly in my cabin and you are so polite that you won't ask for it back. So from now on I'll ration you some jelly daily or when I think you need it."

Grace hands Nathan a giant spoonful of his favorite, Beach Plum Jelly. The very jelly he and Grace made while on Bassett's Island.

Levi has now changed course slightly as land comes into view. He sees a tall structure painted in a spiral fashion.

"Galon do you recognize that structure?"

"A-yah," replies Old Galon. "It is the Cape Hatteras Lighthouse. We'd better stay far offshore, there are many shoals around here."

While they continue their journey Galon begins to explain to Levi.

"Catch and release" is becoming very popular. Companies that sell light fishing tackle primarily used for fresh water fishing are now promoting the idea of using this technique to catch undersize saltwater fish."

"Why don't the fishermen just stay in the ponds and lakes?"

"Well, for years the government has stocked ponds for these weekend fishermen, but they catch all the fish up quickly. Now new fishing schemes are being developed."

"Why are people allowed to target undersize fish and destroy the future stocks?"

"I don't know, but it's hard to understand society anyway. The same people who think that a fish caught by a commercial boat with a net will die, think a fish that is caught with a hook and lifted out of the water with its total body weight pulling on its mouth will do fine. Think about it… when a fish lives in the ocean he is almost neutral in the water, weightless no matter how big he is."

*Billy's Tour of Central
North Carolina*

1. **Harkers Island**
2. **Cedar Island**
3. **Core Creek**
4. **Atlantic**
5. **Cape Lookout**
6. **New Bern**
7. **Morehead City**
8. **Cape Hatteras**
9. **Pamlico Sound**

Chapter Eight

Galon is still explaining to the Speedwell's crew.

"This coast is known as the "Graveyard of the Atlantic" because of all the ships that have foundered and been lost here."

"We should continue south to the next Cape," says Levi. "Perhaps I can find some old charts of this area stored away in our cabin. We can find our way into the sounds with them."

With that Galon takes the wheel while the brothers go into the cabin to find the charts. Charts, drawn long ago by Arthur Barlowe. Levi and Nathan are looking through all their papers and other writings under the bunk very carefully.

Nathan quickly jumps to his feet with the old tattered maps of the Carolina coast. He hands them to Levi who looks carefully at the charts and then brings them up to Galon.

"According to this old map Galon, the next point of land that resembles a cape is called the Cape of Fear."

Galon looks carefully at the very old map.

"That's not right Levi. That Cape is now called Cape Lookout. Cape Fear is much further south."

The Speedwell at Cape Lookout Bight.

Levi heads back to the cabin and spreads the map upon his desk. Carefully he draws a line through the original name and writes Cape Lookout in its place.

The old man can now vaguely make out another towering structure in the distance. As the Speedwell gets closer to the tower, he can see the diamond shaped pattern that tells mariners this is the Cape Lookout Light. Again the ship goes far out to sea to bypass many shoals in the area.

Looking at Levi's old chart it is decided that the Speedwell and her crew will swing in towards land and head back north along the coast to a small cove near the Cape Lookout Light known as the Cape Lookout Bight.

As the Speedwell skirts the Outer Banks, thousands of what appears to be automobile tires litter the beach.

"What is this Galon?" Levi questions with great concern.

"I'm not sure."

The Speedwell continues on her journey, finding the Bight virtually barren of people and vessels this time of year.

Anchoring up in the cove, early in the evening, Levi suggests that in the morning, rather than sailing, they just go ashore and explore the area. Everyone is in agreement that this is the thing to do, and all say their goodnights and head off to their respective hammocks, and Grace retires to her quarters.

Waking early as always, both Galon and Levi set upon the cannons to watch the sun rise. Their view was hampered by the early morning fog that is common in this area at this time of year. The mist is low, close to the water. The top of the lighthouse is barely visible to them.

"The sun seems later this morning, Levi."

"Yes it is, my friend. We are much further west here than we were on the Cape of Cod, so the sun comes up later. The light will last longer into the evening though, because we are much further south. The closer you get to the equator the more even the times of daylight become. As the further away from the equator you get the longer and shorter the days become during the year."

Unseen to the two men, a solitary figure stands high upon a dune on the nearby island. This lonely sentinel has spotted their ship slowly emerging through the early morning mist.

The first sight of the Speedwell to this spirit was the Barlow Family Pirate Flag waving gently in the morning breeze. As the fog dissipated the vessel in all her glory, as an old Bermuda Sloop became quite apparent to this spirit.

Quickly leaving the area to think, this spirit must consider that pirates have been rumored to haunt these islands awaiting the return of

Blackbeard, the legendary King of Pirates. He was slain not far from here at Ocracoke Inlet. The remains of Blackbeard's Flagship, The Queen Ann's Revenge, is also resting on the ocean bottom, not far away.

Soon Nathan is upon the deck joining the old man and Levi.

"Come let us untie the longboat and lower it into the water, so we are ready when Grace gets about."

"I am," barks Grace from the doorway to her cabin.

"I can help too!"

"Alright," says Levi. "Let's get to work."

Quickly the longboat is released and lowered into the water. They all slowly take turns climbing down into the boat. Spending so many days at sea has left their legs unstable. Levi rows ashore slowly. They all drag the heavy longboat aground, above the high tide line, so it won't drift away while they look around the area.

Seeing a walkway built of planking across the dunes Nathan yells.

"Follow me!" And races upon the wooden boardwalk, down past the lighthouse, and across the narrow strip of marsh and land.

The boardwalk ends upon the most beautiful sandy beach. The water here is clear and warm with a greenish hue.

"This place is so beautiful." Nathan says to himself as he sits down on the steps of the boardwalk, waiting for the others to catch up.

Levi and the others walk much more slowly as their legs adjust to the earth. After spending days upon the rocking boat the land does not move at all and the lack of motion makes walking difficult for some people.

Levi talks as they walk.

"You should know that this strip of land was about where our forefather, Arthur Barlowe first started his exploration of the New World in 1584. Look around, this place is as beautiful today as it must have been 400 years ago. As I see it there seem to be few places now that have been protected from society, but this place has survived well."

Stopping almost all the way across the boardwalk they pause to look around.

"The trees, the grasses, the shoreline, it is as beautiful as any place in the world." Grace notes.

"Aye, it is," agrees the old man. We'd better catch up to Nathan or he'll be off on a hunt for beach plums."

Laughing, they head for the end of the walk where Nathan patiently awaits their arrival.

The sand is warm. The waves gently caress the shore. Together again they begin walking northeast following the beach.

Along the water's edge are surf fishermen. They are fishing for flounder and whatever else they can catch. Most have special trucks equipped to drive on the beach. While walking along Nathan has many questions about these fishermen.

"What do you think they do with their fish?"

Galon answers quickly. "These people have ice chests to store their catch. They probably cook some and take the rest home for their family and friends."

"That is great. Fishing for fun is a good pass time, but none should be intentionally wasted." Quips Nathan.

"So Nathan." The old man goes on, "If you saw someone catching many small fish, what would you tell them?"

"Why I would probably tell them to try another spot, or at least to use a bigger hook. A bigger hook would make it much more difficult to catch a smaller fish."

Levi changing the subject makes some observations of his own.

"I can not believe how beautiful this area is. Did you notice the wild horses on the next island?"

"Yes." Grace quickly replies. "I think that is called Shackleford Banks.

They keep walking along the beach for several miles. Occasionally noticing a figure will appear in the distance, seeming to look in their direction, then go down in between the sand hills, out of sight.

"Nathan! Why don't you and Grace walk over the dunes and then split up, and walk in the same direction as us to see if you can discover what this person is doing." Suggests Levi.

"Okay." Nathan was ready to go.

"Lets go Grace!"

And he ran off into the dunes. Grace looked at Levi.

"I'd really like to do as you want, but my feet are tired and they have no interest."

Everyone laughed as Nathan disappeared from view.

Continuing to walk they soon see Nathan come into view again. Yelling to them from high atop a dune he declared.

"I saw him! I saw him! He has no shadow. Come quick."

As the trio gets to Nathan, Grace asks.

"Which way did he go?"

Nathan points ahead of them, across the sand.

"That way."

"No! That can't be." Levi says. "There are no footprints."

Looking back Levi realizes that they have left no impression in the sand either.

On top of the next dune the figure slowly comes into sight. He is a middle-aged man, dressed in khaki colored work clothes, very neat and crisp. He wears a ball cap that shades his face.

"Hello there," he speaks softly, slowly and very knowingly.

"I see that you are like myself, spirits that have chosen to stay behind for some reason."

Levi answers. "Yes, we are from the North. The Cape of Cod actually. We decided to take our ship, the Speedwell South for the winter to avoid the ice and snow. Some of us are from this time, yet my brother and I have somehow been misplaced in time. We were aboard our ship, during the time of the Revolutionary War, when we were caught up in a terrible storm that deposited us into our future, your present, as spirits. Our adventures have not brought to light what one would have thought that such an advanced society is truly capable of."

"What do you mean?" Asks the spirit of the Banks.

"What I mean is that a society that has the capabilities of developing all the technological marvels it has should certainly be capable of taking care of the coastal habitat that everyone seems to want to live right next to."

"Perhaps you are right." If you have time I'll fill you in on this part of North Carolina."

"That sounds good to me." Levi goes on. "But first let me introduce my crew and myself. This here is Grace, a woman of these times that joined us on the Cape of Cod. She has lived in the great state of North Carolina for a time. And this handsome, elderly gentleman is Galon, a gardener extraordin-aire and lifetime shellfisherman. This is my brother Nathan who fought alongside me during our heyday in the Revolutionary War, at the Battle of Nantucket. We lost the battle, but managed to go back and capture the British ship anyway, with the help of many others. Those were the days. Right Nathan? Things were so different back then. My name is Levi, the Speedwell is, well was my ship, now it is our home."

"And a fine ship she is," says the spirit. It's nice to make your acquaintance. I am simply known as Billy. My given name was William, but I'm Billy. My home during my life was not far from here, just across the Sound, in a small fishing village. Many of my family are still there and others have gone on. I have chosen to stay along these banks for a time. I help guide the souls of fishermen and seafarers that die here to go on their way.

I myself passed on not far from here in a boating accident. A rouge wave over turned our boat so quickly that we hardly noticed. Rouge waves are very dangerous, especially when they are approaching a shoal area or the shoreline itself. But all is not lost.

During the summer on the Fourth of July, the holiday that celebrates the war that you and your brother fought in, many locals make a special day trip to the Outer Banks to celebrate this holiday. While they do not know of my presence, it's great to see them all and hear what's going on."

After making acquaintances everyone sat upon the dunes. They can see the waters of Core Sound very clearly. Nathan is quick to ask questions.

"So Billy, I see there are many people here in the water walking about."

"Yes, they are mostly clamming, but some may be cast netting for shrimp."

"How can that be?" Nathan asks. "I've read many stories and have heard many tales of the waters in this area. All of the stories tell of the dreaded sting rays that injure some people, and cripple others by driving a sharp pointed barb into any part of a persons body."

"The stories are true, Nathan, but fishermen using gill nets to harvest flounder in the shallow inshore waters keep this specie in check.

Society as a whole doesn't understand the use of gill nets. This is a very selective fishery. The mesh size allows the smaller fish to swim through the net and only large fish are harvested. Occasionally a sea bird becomes entangled in the net. They are usually released unharmed. If the use of these nets is curtailed, the people who will

**Tires from artificial reefs off the
coast, litter the shoreline.**

suffer the most will be the new coastal residents that have moved here recently. They don't realize how quickly their recreational activities will be affected when it is unsafe for them and their children step into the local waters."

"These sound like social problems to me." States the old man.

"I suppose they are. And there are plenty of these problems coming about in this area, at this time." Billy said.

Levi goes on.

"Well, perhaps if you are available to guide us you could take us through the local waters and give us an education!"

"That would be great. Things are quiet here now and I would enjoy seeing the sounds and rivers again."

The group turns and heads back towards the cove where the Speedwell is anchored.

"Do you know anything about all the tires along the beach?" Asks Grace.

"Yes. What a site they are. They were part of an artificial reef built offshore for sport fishing activities. These reefs were supposed to attract marine growth and become an artificial habitat. These tires have been under the ocean for years and are now washing upon the beaches. They have little growth on them and are being hauled away by the government. There are many other structures and wrecks that have been intentionally dumped in the ocean, in this area.

A lot of this debris is damaging fishing gear to say nothing of the environment. While this coast has been known, for centuries, with great respect as the Graveyard of the Atlantic, it is becoming widely known now as the **Junkyard of the Ocean.**"

Chapter Nine

The group is nearing the cove where the Speedwell is anchored. Nathan has an idea.

"Would anyone like to have a fire tonight? Grace and I could go gather some clams. I sure miss the smell of them cooking."

"That sounds like a real good idea. I've not had anyone to visit with for some time now."

Reaching the cove they all drag the longboat to the water's edge so Nathan and Grace can row to the ship and get Grace's clam rake and the lighter that Old Galon had given Nathan when the brothers first met him upon Bassett's Island.

Nathan puts one oar in a slot, in the middle of the stern of the longboat and begins to skillfully propel the longboat towards the Speedwell.

"What are you doing?" Grace asks.

"Why this is called sculling. It was a very common way of propelling a small boat in the past. It is probably a lost art now."

Arriving at the Speedwell, Grace climbs aboard.

"My rake is just inside my cabin, Nathan. I will get the lighter for you. It is right by the stove. Be right back." And she disappeared from view.

Quickly she returns with the items and climbed carefully down, back into the longboat. She pushed the longboat off and once again Nathan sculls the boat along quickly. Reaching the shore in no time, they drag the longboat up the beach and secure it. Grace picked up her clam rake and pointed out to Nathan.

"There are no rocks around here to circle the fire. You will have to dig a shallow pit, and build a high spot in the middle of it to place the clams on."

With that Grace headed off, down the beach, and into the shallow waters to gather a few clams. Nathan walked into the nearby bushes to gather dry wood for his fire. After gathering several pieces of suitable wood and kindling, he got on his hands and knees and proceeded to dig a fine pit, with a nice high spot in the middle to steam the clams. He could almost smell them cooking in his mind.

Galon, Levi and Billy found a large old log and have dragged it down near Nathan's pit.

"This log will make a fine seat," Galon proudly announced.

Setting upon the log Levi smiles in agreement. Galon and Billy follow suit.

"Billy, do bay scallops still grow around here?" Galon inquires.

"Well, they still are very plentiful in Core Sound, but in many other areas here they have not done as well. There are a few small beds remaining in Bogue Sound and some in the area of Back Sound. Scallop populations decreased dramatically a few years back after a red tide.

Many of the fishermen feel that the loss of these shellfish, which have grown in the sounds of North Carolina for centuries, can only be a sign of things to come. This appears to be a direct result of shoddy coastal development."

Grace has returned now with a few clams for Nathan.

"Nathan, get your fire going. It will be dark soon."

Nathan immediately works on building the fire. As soon as the wood begins to burn Nathan carefully places the clams that Grace has found on the high spot in the fire. They are surrounded by the fire. The clams will steam nicely. Nathan finds a small log and sits down wind of the fire, smelling the essence of the clams steaming in their own juices.

Grace now sits upon the ground leaning against the larger log.

"Billy, do you know why these scallops are so much smaller than the bay scallops up North?"

"Perhaps it's related to the shallow waters and crop density. The exchange of waters in these sounds is very restricted." He explains.

Grace goes on.

"I just raked some scallops up and they look to be the same shellfish, only somewhat smaller."

"Well Grace, I'm not a biologist, but I do know that they are the same scallop. Only in the South this scallop spawns when the water temperature is falling, and in the North the same shellfish spawns while the water temperature is rising. The really weird difference is that these scallops, although virtually identical, will choose to lie on one side of its shell in the North and the other side of its shell in the South. This is very noticeable to the people who open these shellfish, as the topside of the shell is usually much darker and has more growth than the bottom side of the shell. But there also may be other new reasons for lack of growth."

"What would they be?" Questioned Levi.

"There has been a lot of new technology developed in the field of aquaculture in our sounds. This is supposed to be like gardening in the ocean.

The way it works is that a person with a lease (rented ocean bottom) from the state to a certain area of bottom can grow shellfish. This sounds like a really good idea before you give it some serious thought.

It is only natural for a person to plant as many shellfish in an area as they possibly can. But, high-density plantings increase the risk of shellfish diseases. Hard clams have always seemed very hearty, but now they have a disease of their own. QPX is its name and it has taken an unknown toll on the clam population along the East Coast. This disease was quickly traced back to the aquaculture industry.

More important is the fact that these gardeners of the sea are not growing vegetables, they are growing animals. Animals that feed from the surrounding area. A single oyster can filter 250 gallons of water per day. Removing the food it needs to survive on from the water in this process.

Imagine this, a person or business plants one million shellfish per acre. That is not uncommon. One million oysters can filter the food that they eat daily from the local waters that flow back and forth across the shellfish lease. This means that 250 million gallons of water per day, per acre may be stripped of the necessary nutrients that support the wild and natural fishery. This is food for scallops and many other small fish, shrimp and shellfish that is taken from the public waters to feed a private individual's farm. This practice does not make sense when inspected closely.

The waters here are shallow and have a restricted tidal flow. These shallow waters are quickly stripped of their nutrients by these high-density plantings. The affects upon the wild fishery become more obvious all the time. Aquaculture belongs in areas of deeper water with large volumes of water exchange. Even then it should be monitored very closely.

Years ago in Japan many people died as a result of aquacultured scallops. These scallops carried an illness called PSP - Paralytic Shellfish Poisoning."

Changing the subject, Billy asks.

"Galon, you have fished all your life. What do you think has led to many of these social problems in our business?"

"That is a very complicated question Billy. I'll be glad to give you my opinion."

The old man pauses for a moment to think.

"First and foremost is the jealousy and animosity that seems to be directed towards the full time fishermen no matter who or where they are. Weekenders have a very hard time understanding why a full time fisherman can be so successful, while they may not do near as well.

Fishing is not a momentary event for a full time fisherman. There is no way to learn this business without devoting many years to it, and living the life of it. If you don't live the life of a full time fisherman, you can never understand it.

The big trouble comes in when people who don't understand the commercial fishing business try to regulate it. Time and time again full time fisherman are blamed for things that are beyond their control. Government officials sometimes get worn down and find it easier to *"pacify the ignorance"* of the masses, than to do what is right for the coastal community."

"Those are very interesting observations Galon." Levi comments.

"It is late and we should rest. Tomorrow we can sail down the sounds and Billy can share more of his vast knowledge of this beautiful coast with us."

Nathan's fire has burned out. He begins to fill in his pit. Then he and Grace drag the longboat down the beach into the water.

Billy and Levi talk at the water's edge.

"Send the longboat for me at sunrise. I'll be here waiting to join you."

"Okay." Levi replies and is the last to climb in the longboat.

Soon the crew is back aboard the Speedwell for the evening. They wearily head for their quarters. It has been a very long day.

Billy at the helm of the Speedwell.

Chapter Ten

Before sunrise, in the early light of day, Levi rowed slowly towards shore. He was excited about this day's journey with Billy and has risen while his crew is still resting. Billy waits patiently on the shore. He too looks forward to this trip back through familiar surroundings. When Levi arrived on the shore, Billy quickly climbed into the stern of the longboat. Levi then rowed back towards the Speedwell. Not a word had been spoken.

"Morning Billy." Levi speaking first, as he looked around to get his bearings.

Billy returned the greeting as he looked closely at the Speedwell and the flag that she was flying.

"Good day, Levi. I really like the appearance of your ship. I've seen a display that closely resembles this ship in the Maritime Museum, in Beaufort. Many of these coastal trading vessels were built here in North Carolina at one time."

"Yes, I believe the Speedwell may have been built here too." He replies while still rowing.

"Tell me Levi, why do you fly a flag very similar to a pirate flag?"

"The flag is a family heirloom. A forefather of the Barlow family made it. Captain Edward Barlow created this flag while preparing to battle Captain Kidd upon the Indian Ocean in the late 1690's."

"No! You've got to be kidding me."

"It is true. Captain Edward kept a very accurate log and Kidd was eventually hanged for this and other unscrupulous deeds. Kidd denied everything to the end."

The longboat is now alongside the old sloop. Billy and Levi climb aboard. They tie the longboat to the stern of the Speedwell. The crew is up and about on deck getting right to their duties.

Galon and Nathan are turning the old windlass to raise the anchor, while Grace has climbed into the rigging to secure the topsail. Levi and Billy hoist the mainsail. They feel that this will be sufficient to power the Speedwell through the day.

The wind is light from the southwest. It's a perfect morning as Billy takes control of the helm and guides the old sloop "Down East" through Core Sound.

Grace and Nathan climb back into the rigging again to enjoy the scenery. Harkers Island is on their left as they sail along swiftly. Soon Davis Island appears to their left. As they pass the area known as Davis Shore, Levi asks Billy about the fishing activity going on in the distance.

"What are these fishermen catching?"

"Oh, they are harvesting crabs. Lots of crabs. Crabs are very important to the coastal economy here, but then so are fish, shrimp, and shellfish. All of these fisheries are equally important, regardless which one may be more productive at any given time.

The fishermen are catching crabs in traps called crab pots right now, but at another time they may tow crab trawls behind their boats.

Over towards the Banks the waters are very shallow. These shoals that go on from here to Cape Hatteras are among the most productive natural shellfish beds and nursery areas in the Continental United States."

"Why is that?" Asks Levi.

"The islands from Ocracoke Island south to Shackleford Banks are basically uninhabited. There is no development and very little pollution here."

Billy is now sailing the Speedwell past Atlantic, his home during his life. He looks longingly towards the fish house where he spent so much of his time with his family and friends. Levi realizes Billy's longings and says.

"Don't even think about it! Time passes quickly as a spirit. Nathan and I have been spirits for over two hundred years and it seems like only yesterday that we ate supper together at our family

Hauling crab pots in Core Sound.

homestead in a little place called Barlow's Landing."

"Where was that?" Billy asked.

"A long way from here. It is a small harbor in the North, in a bay called Buzzards Bay."

"I know Buzzards Bay." He said. "We used to tie up in New Bedford occasionally. We felt that the Southern boats were treated poorly there."

"I'm sorry to hear that. Do you think society will ever realize that a person's time as a mortal on this earth is very limited and should not be wasted on trivial matters like prejudices?"

"I hope so!" Billy quickly replies as he guides the sloop through the narrow channel between Cedar Island and the shoals along the Banks. He has decided to sail up towards the Neuse River.

"Levi, I'm going to take us around Cedar Island and up the Neuse River, towards a city called New Bern, then we can return to Cape Lookout by traveling down the Intracoastal Waterway for a time. This should give you a basic idea of things that may interest you in the Central Coastal District of North Carolina."

Nathan and Grace peer into the distance. The waters have been changing in clarity since passing Cedar Island. Climbing down they go to question Billy about this.

"Billy, why is the water becoming so murky?"

**Trawler churning oxygen into
the coastal environment.**

"Well, there is a lot of silt in the water. It comes down stream for hundreds of miles and settles out of the water column in the estuaries, where the salt waters and fresh waters meet. This silt smothers many species, while encouraging the growth of new and unusual life forms so to speak. I'm not too familiar with the recent scientific terms."

Grace sees a large shrimp boat in the distance. She scurries back up into the rigging to watch. Almost immediately she returns to the deck.

"Billy, that shrimp boat has a trail of silt behind it."

"Yes. Yes it does Grace. But the shrimp boat did not put the silt there. They are gently towing their nets across the area, putting the silt back up into the water column to hopefully give the substrate a chance to recover some life giving oxygen. As the boats tow these nets a large amount of air is churned into the water by the boat's propeller as it cavitates in the water. This helps to combat a condition called "low dissolved oxygen." This is a very serious threat to our rivers and sounds. Hundreds of shrimp and crab trawlers have spent thousands of hours trying to keep this area productive and free from the smothering silt.

The biggest problem for these fishermen is the lack of understanding by the general public. Many people have pre-conceived notions about trawling in the sounds."

Grace climbs back into the rigging to enjoy the scenery once again with Nathan.

"Nathan." She says. "This is a very beautiful place, unspoiled and pristine. It's hard to believe that these estuaries are in such terrible condition."

Old Galon has been sitting quietly. After listening to Billy, he speaks.

"Ya know, these folks better wake up! If these contaminants are allowed to build up, a change may occur, causing more unwanted algae growth. These growths may build up and spread down the river, to the grass beds along the banks. The algae growths may damage the grass beds. Without the grass beds to hold the sand there will be serious erosion problems. The Barrier Islands could deteriorate quickly. I know that this doesn't sound likely, but it has happened many times before."

Going on the old man adds.

"Perhaps if things go differently the area will just fill in with the toxins and silt to become totally unproductive like a place called Plymouth we recently visited. Pamlico Sound is just a larger version of that harbor. There are many more rivers and tributaries here, almost all of them contributing toxins and pollutants."

"This is a very large body of water, but it is relatively shallow. I'm sure that you are right in your thoughts of how quickly it could become stagnant." Billy speaks softly as he looks around.

The Speedwell is now passing an area known as South River on their left. Billy points in the direction of the village of South River.

"That is a typical fishing community. The shellfish beds are occasionally closed because of runoff and pollution. The fishermen turn to trawling many months of the year. Society doesn't realize the importance of the hours that these men spend trying to maintain a productive fishery for everyone. This may prove futile in time. As inland development increases more waste will be dumped into the river systems from sewer plants, as well as from road runoff and farm residue. The fragile ecosystems of the Neuse River between the village of South River and the town called Oriental, on the opposite side of this wide, shallow river will certainly be the next victims of shoddy coastal development. There are many toxins that will damage this estuary. Some are already in the rivers and streams that lead here. In time they will eventually flow to this general area and begin to settle out of the water column.

As we sail further up this river you'll begin to notice more vegetation growing in the waters. In the smaller streams and creeks vegetation is very thick and reduces water flow. As the vegetation dies and breaks down, further changes occur.

Fish kill on the Neuse River.

None of these things are good. These waters frequently have major fish kills."

"Why don't the fish just swim down stream?" Levi asks.

"I don't know. But I do know that they usually die because of low dissolved oxygen or something called Pfiesteria."

"What is that?" Galon questions.

Billy goes on.

"I'm not quite sure how to explain it, but it can affect people too."

"How?" Galon questions.

"Some people suffer short term memory loss, while others suffer serious rashes. These rashes almost appear like burns, but are actually a virus that can be treated."

The Speedwell has now picked up some speed as it sails up the Neuse River towards New Bern. When Grace and Nathan can see the city in the distance, Nathan calls down to Billy.

"Go over there." Pointing towards a giant patch of brownish colored water. Now sailing through the brown water it is not difficult for all to see the millions of dead and dying fish. Some weakly swim in circles, while others float belly up in the water. Sores can be seen on the undersides of these fish as they drift along.

"Billy, what can this be?" Levi asks, never having seen such a sight.

Vegetation cokes small creeks.

"Pfiesteria.   It is actually a single celled dinoflagellate, a very small critter that has been here for centuries.   Some unknown type of pollution or a combination of pollutants cause them to act very differently, becoming aggressive and killing fish. They may also be responsible for the increase in marine related illnesses in this part of the state recently."

"Billy, perhaps it is time we head back to Cape Lookout. I'm sure that this Pfiesteria can't affect us, but there is little point in our getting Nathan upset again."

While Billy heads the sloop back down the river the direction of the wind changes to gently fill the sails of the Speedwell.

Billy has noticed something odd and speaks to Levi about it.

"This seems very strange to me. No matter where we go we seem to have a fair wind and tide."

"Yes, I agree it is very odd. We have had a fair wind to sail with ever since we left Bassett's Island."

Billy skillfully sails the ship down the river and into Adams Creek, the beginning of their short voyage in the Intracoastal Waterway.

"This is a short cut back to the Cape." Billy announces to all.

From the rigging the area appears very unspoiled. The land has been somewhat developed but in large parcels. Grace can read a sign on the shore and begins to read out loud so all can hear.

"Single home sites for sale. Large lots. Call Weyerhaeuser Real Estate."

Seeing this sign Nathan inquired of Grace.

"Grace, why so much land for one home?"

"This is a way to lessen the impact of coastal development. There is much more open space left around these homes than in other developments. Few companies are willing to go to this extreme to develop land sensibly."

Now entering the man made section of the canal Billy yells to Nathan and Grace.

"Watch near the shore. I'm sure that you'll see some deer and perhaps even a bear or two."

Soon after Nathan pokes Grace.

"Look over there." Pointing into the woods. Sure enough, a deer leaps into the water and swims across the creek right in front of their sloop.

"That is so beautiful!" Grace comments to Nathan.

Coming in to view now, on the left, is a wooden fishing pier. Many people sit on the pier talking and fishing. A large sign upon the shore reads Masons Marina. Directly across the canal a large man stands near a skiff, calling a dog in the distance.

"HEEEE YA!" "HEEEE YA!"

Next to this man are baskets of clams and a clam rake. Grace gets Nathan's attention and points towards the large man.

"That man over there. I knew him during my life. He's called "Big John", he's a clamming man."

Entering the Newport River dolphins swim all about the Speedwell, jumping and splashing in the water. Nathan just watches in awe.

Soon Billy guides the ship down the Newport River, then under the high rise bridge at Morehead City. Huge piles of wood chips can be seen at this port.

"Billy, what do they do here?" Asks Levi.

"This is a busy import and export site. Goods from here are shipped all over the world. Those wood chips will be paper someday or even perhaps glued back together in sheets of partical board for building. I know this port is a busy place, but I really don't know too much of what takes place here."

The Speedwell and her crew now head for Beaufort Inlet and passes through into the ocean. Cape Lookout is visible in the distance. The ship moves along smoothly in the clear waters of the ocean again.

Coming into the cove where the Speedwell had been anchored in the morning, Billy turns the sloop into the wind as once again Nathan lowers the anchor. Grace climbs the rigging to release the topsail, while Levi and Galon quickly lower the mainsail.

As the sun sets in the distance the longboat is lowered again into the water. Levi is ready to row ashore with Billy. He climbs down and sits in the stern.

"I can not thank you enough for showing us around the area today."

"Levi, it was no bother at all. I've enjoyed this day very much. It was nice to sail around the sounds again."

"Will you spend the winter? " Billy asks as the longboat reaches the shore.

" Probably, I think we would be safe from snow and ice here. I'll have to talk it over with the others. Well, I must go rest; it has been a long day. Farewell for now."

Levi rows back towards the Speedwell watching Billy fade slowly into the evening light.

Be sure to look for Levi and his crew on new adventures.

Help turn the tide

Bottom Paint...

These special paints have but one purpose; to discourage unwanted marine growth.

They must be treated carefully. Caution must be taken while handling and applying these dangerous chemicals. The preparation of the bottom of a boat for another coat of bottom paint can be a very hazardous task. Read the labels on the paint can before you open it. Be careful working with the paint that is already on the hull. The dust that is produced from these paints contains dangerous toxins. It is very important that another non-toxic method be found to accomplish the same task.

Many of the toxins in these paints will remain in the coastal environment for a long time.

Exotic Species (and Diseases)...

These are species of marine life that are not natural to a certain part of the world.

Many times when an exotic species is unintentionally transplanted to a new area there are no predators to control its development. These exotic species have the opportunity to reproduce at an alarming rate, often severely reducing natural populations of other species in a given area. The control of exotic species must be monitored seriously. The detrimental affects of an exotic species can happen very quickly in the ocean. Often these species and illnesses remain unnoticed by everyone for long periods of time.

Trawling...

This is the use of funnel shaped nets towed behind a boat to harvest food fish and shellfish from the ocean.

Fishermen during recent years have accepted many changes to net designs, put forward by the scientific community, that allow small and unwanted fish to escape from these nets while they are being fished. Other designs used in some areas also allow for turtles to be excluded from these nets. Full time fishermen are doing everything in their power to preserve the habitat, and to encourage the recovery of fish stocks. This is their livelihood and it is only natural that they, as a group, are very concerned with the continued protection of the natural fisheries and spawning grounds.

Catch and Release...

This is a relatively new scheme to the coastal area. The idea is to target undersize fish and catch them for enjoyment, human enjoyment.

This scheme has been developed to sell more lightweight fishing tackle. The effect this type of fishing is having on stocks, that are now recovering, is not good. These fish are being targeted and often injured severely for the fun of it. This type of fishing activity is not consistent with the policies of today that promote the rebuilding of fish stocks.

Harbors and Sounds...

These are the coastal areas that accumulate the unseen wastes of society.

Plymouth Harbor in Massachusetts is simply an example of the many harbors along the coast that need attention.

North Carolina's Pamlico Sound is so large that it is virtually an inland sea. This body of water and its tributaries are undoubtedly amongst the most important Eco-systems in this country. Society must take responsibility for this huge habitat. We must start to look at the big picture. The whole area rather than segments of this Eco-system. This particular sound and its tributaries are suffering rapid degradation as different user groups try to develop new schemes to promote this area as something other than what it is, and should remain. Country living on large rural tracts of land.

Recycle Water...

Society must develop acceptable ways to recycle a significant amount of the fresh water that we currently waste.

We use most water only once then send it on its way through a sewer plant to be processed and disposed of. Perhaps it is time society considers new methods of water use and disposal. Thus, encouraging the development of new technology for home water recycling. Washing machines would be a good place to start. If water from this process alone were reduced, coastal sewer processing plants may regain some of their effectiveness.

This is only a stopgap measure. New ways of dealing with waste must be developed and quickly. The dumping of wastes into the ocean will have to be curtailed at some point. Society can not survive without fresh water, and we are currently dumping it into the ocean much faster than it could ever replenish itself.

Social Problems...

Society has always suffered from growing pains. User groups of any shared resource have always tried to convince society, or at least it's leaders, that their group deserves a bigger part of a given resource or other special considerations.

This usually leads to further discontent and resentment and does nothing for the resource in question. Leaders need to make a firm stand against changes that are not backed up by real facts and historical figures.

Marine science is a relatively new field and often full time fishermen are more aware of causes and effects than one might think. They have to be. This is their livelihood. Other larger groups of weekend fishermen with limited information often try to change rules and regulations without putting forward or knowing all the pertinent information. When this not successful, they only try harder, often becoming bitter and obsessive.

There is no solution to this problem other than education.

Glossary

Aft – The back; stern of a ship.

Aquaculture – The controlled, cultured growing, by private industry of shellfish and finfish in fresh or salt water.

Artificial Reef – A manmade structure on the ocean's bottom created to attract marine growth, fish and as a marine life habitat.

Awe – The feeling or emotion inspired by contemplation of something sublime.

Banks – Barrier Island

Barb – (Sting Ray Barb) A piece of solid matter, long in proportion to its thickness which impedes or obstructs. Used as a defense.

Barrier Island(s) – An island between the ocean and a river, sound or bay.

Bay Scallop – A shellfish; a marine bivalve, having the edge of its shell in the form of a series of curves.

Beach Plum – Or shore plum, tall shrub bearing tart, purple to yellow plums, 2 inches (5 cm) in diameter, fruit used in jelly or jam. Shrub grows in sandy soil along northeastern coast of North America. Propagated by seeds or root cuttings in the autumn.

Bermuda Sloop – A one-masted ship with a fore and aft rig.

Bight – A bend in a coast line forming an open bay or small bay between two highlands.

Bilge – The broadest part of a boat's bottom, on which it can rest when aground. Water will leak, spill or be washed into the boat's bilge.

Blue Fin Tuna – A large finfish of the tuna family. Also known as a horse mackerel.

Bluff – An area rising steeply or boldly over the water's edge.

Bottom Paint – A toxic substance used on boats to prevent the growth of marine life. Applied yearly in the spring, prior to use in water.

Bow – The front part of a ship.

Bowsprit – A large boom or spar running out from the bow of a ship to carry its sails forward.

Breakwater – Any structure, man made or natural to break the force of the waves.

Broadside – The entire side of a ship above the water line.

By-catch – Other marine life caught while trawling. Usually released unharmed.

Cape of Cod – What the now Cape Cod was once called.

Cast Net – A hand held fish net, thrown, hurled into water used to harvest fish and shrimp.

Cast-off – To leave; turn from anchored area.

Catch and Release – Relatively new fishing scheme.

Channel – The bed of a stream, a water course, the deepest part of a bay or harbor.

Chart – A map of any part of the sea, river, sound or bay; for use of mariners.

Coastal Mariner (s) – Someone who sails on a merchant ship.

Coastal Trader (s) – A person or boat employed to trade on the coast.

Codium (Spike Grass) – An "exotic" plant. A jointed, pulpy, green, marine alga sometimes called spike grass. It attaches itself to the exposed shells, chiefly to the oyster and to the bay scallop. As it grows rapidly, much faster than the shell it attaches to, it eventually drags the host shell off. There is presently no known cure.

Crab Trawl – A boat with net that harvests blue crabs.

Demise – Death.

"Down East" – Coastal area of land in Central North Carolina that jets/extends to the east through the sounds.

Exotic – Foreign; belonging to another part of the world.

Fleet (s) – A company of ships, boats or vessels together.

Fish Stocks – Counts of fish and shellfish in an area; for records.

Flounder – A flat sea fish with both his eyes on topside of body.

Fluke – The broad part of an anchor. A flounder.

Fore – The front/bow part of a ship.

Fore and Aft – The entire length of a ship.

Foundered – To sink by filling with water; disable.

Furled – To roll up or secure to something; as a sail.

Garbage Barge – Term used to describe a container barge towed off shore, filled with public garbage and debris.

George's Banks – A shoal area off the New England coast that is a productive fishing ground.

Gill Net – A fish net, used to harvest fish..

Gill (s) – The respiratory organ of aquatic animals, especially fish.

"Grave Yard of the Atlantic" – Areas of the Atlantic Ocean that are prone to causing shipwrecks.

Helm – The apparatus for steering a ship.

Intracoastal Waterway – This runs from Cape Cod Massachusetts to Florida. A chain of man made canals that connect various sounds and bays.

Knot (s) – A nautical mile = 2,025 yards.

Larvae – Reproductive eggs in the marine habitat.

Long Boat – A large oared boat usually carried by a merchant sailing ship.

Low Dissolved Oxygen – Areas in rivers, bays and sounds where the life sustaining oxygen is serverly depleted for natural or unnatural reasons.

Massachusetts Maritime Academy (MMA) – A college; one of only 8 in all the US. Graduates Merchant Marines. It is located on Buzzards Bay on Cape Cod.

Mast – A long round piece of timber, raised vertically on the keel of a ship to support the sails.

Master's License – A Captain's permit to operate a vessel or ship.

Mayflower – The ship the Pilgrims sailed to the New World in.

Merchant Marine – Same as Coastal Trader, but with government papers.

Muck hole – Moist mud; anything filthy or vile.

Narrative – A written story; tale to document an event or journey.

New World – Referred to the unexplored or undeveloped America.

Nor' Easter – Coastal storm that blows primarily from the northeast.

Nuclear Power Plant – Type of energy facility that generates and passes power to another place or places. Nuclear fuel being used.

Nursery Area – A place where young fish and shellfish are born and raised.

Ocean Outfall – Sewer plant discharge extended into the ocean.

Patriot State – Training ship at the Massachusetts Maritime Academy, a merchant marine college in Massachusetts.

Pfistiria – A single celled dinoflagellate.

Plimouth – The colonial spelling of Plymouth.

Power Plant – A facility from which energy is produced and passed to other places to power. A ship, boat or vessel's power.

PSP/Paralytic Shellfish Poisoning – A deadly illness caused by a marine dinoflagellate.

QPX – Stands for Quahog Parasite Unknown. A new clam disease.

Quarters – Lodging aboard a boat.

Red Tide – A toxin alga bloom that occurs naturally.

Replica – A copy of an original piece, a boat, an article.

Rigging – The cordage or ropes by which the masts of a ship are supported, and the sails extended or furled.

Rouge Wave – An unusually large wave caused by seismic activity or extreme weather conditions thousands of miles away.

School of Fish – A great number of fish together.

Scow – A flat-bottomed boat with broad square ends.

Scull – An oar used at the stern of a boat to propel it; thus sculling.

Sextant – An instrument for measuring angular distance between objects; used especially at sea for determining latitude and longitude.

Shoal (s) – Shallow areas of water.

Shoddy Coastal Development – Term used; The development of land that degrades the coastal environment.

Sound – A straight or narrow passage of water.

Spawn – To produce or deposit (eggs); reproduction in the marine habitat.

Spirit (s) – Imaginary ghost like figures. They have no shadows.

Stern – The back part of a ship.

Sting Ray – Large winged fish with a flexible tail and a barb.

Surf Fishermen – Those not using boats to fish; from the beach or surf they fish.

Three-Masted Schooner – A three masted ship with a fore and aft rig.

Topsail –A sail set on the topmast.

Trawling – The act or process of fishing with a net towed behind a boat.

Watch – Period of time during which part of the crew of a ship is on duty while others sleep.

Weekender – A person or persons who occasionally participate in an activity that is not their livelihood.

Windless – Horizontal cylinder or roller by means of which a heavy anchor is raised.

The "Speedwell" Foundation is a non-profit organization that has been established to generate interest in the coastal environmental problems existing in many areas today. Our goal is to encourage all people to help identify and seek new solutions to these problems.

The avenue chosen to promote our goal is through education and example. The education will be through short stories, pamphlets, and example. Our long term goal is to recover the coastal environmental habitat that has been unintentionally destroyed by society in general. The Foundation intends to build a replica of the Revolutionary War "Pirate" sloop, the Speedwell, as spoke to in the book, The Battle of Nantucket. We believe that this small sloop, one of the smallest to actually participate in a battle during the Revolutionary War, will make an ideal platform to develop interest in this cause. Eventually a tour program will be developed to help people understand the unseen changes taking place just under the surface of the waters in our coastal areas.

While funding is a major concern and tax-deductible contributions are always needed, we would also like to encourage you, the reader, to participate. Please feel free to advise us with your comments and suggestions. It may only take one thought, one suggestion to begin to find the solutions. Be sure to include your address as timely notices will be sent to you as we grow.

There are no membership fees or dues needed to become involved. We ask you to join with us to help promote these goals. We will make a difference!

To make donations, suggestions or to inquire, please write The "Speedwell" Foundation, P.O. Box 409, Beaufort, North Carolina 28516-0409.